BY VICTOR HUGO RETOLD BY L. L. OWENS ILLUSTRATED BY GREG REBIS

LIBRARIAN REVIEWER
Allyson A.W. Lyga
MS, Library Media/Graphic Novel Consultant

READING CONSULTANT
Mark DeYoung
Classroom Teac

www.raintreepublishers.co.uk
Visit our website to find out more information about Raintree books.

To order:
Phone 0845 6044371
Fax +44 (0) 1865 312263
Email myorders@raintreepublishers.co.uk

Customers from outside the UK please telephone +44 1865 312262

Raintree is an imprint of Capstone Global Library Limited, a company incorporated in England and Wales having its registered office at 7 Pilgrim Street, London, EC4V 6LB – Registered company number: 6695582

First published by Stone Arch Books in 2007
First published in hardback in the United Kingdom in 2009
First published in paperback in the United Kingdom in 2010

Art Director: Heather Kindseth
Cover Graphic Designer: Heather Kindseth and Kay Fraser
Interior Graphic Designer: Heather Kindseth
Edited in the UK by Laura Knowles
Printed and bound in China by Leo Paper Products Ltd

ISBN 978-1406212471 (hardback)
13 12 11 10 09
10 9 8 7 6 5 4 3 2 1

ISBN 978-1406213492 (paperback)
14 13 12 11
10 9 8 7 6 5 4

British Library Cataloguing in Publication Data
Owens, L. L.
The Hunchback of Notre Dame. -- (Graphic revolve)
741.5-dc22
A full catalogue record for this book is available from the British Library.

TABLE OF CONTENTS

INTRODUCING . . .

QUASIMODO

ESMERALDA

CLAUDE FROLLO

FLEUR-DE-LYS

SISTER GUDULE

MASTER JACQUES
COPPENOLE

CHAPTER 1
FESTIVAL OF FOOLS
It is 1482. All of Paris is celebrating the Festival of Fools in the shadow of the Cathedral of Notre Dame.

Gather around, everyone, for the game of Pope of Fools!

Let's elect the Pope!
How do we choose, Coppenole?
It's simple. People stick their heads through a hole.
The person with the ugliest face wins!
So, who shall go first?

RRRRRIP!
Each contestant must sit on a chair and poke their head through a hole in the curtain.

What do you think?
He's not ugly enough!
And this one?
NOOOOOOOO

He's a little better!
BOOOOOOO
Next!
Now that is ugly!
She wins!
Let's see just one more. You don't want to miss this one!

Good people of Paris. I give you your Pope of Fools!

OOOOOOOOOOOOOOOOOOHHHH
It's Quasimodo!
He rings the bells all night.
The hunchback of Notre Dame!

Hear, hear!
Huzzah!

The poor fool looks happy, but I feel sorry for him.
A face that only a mother could love.
HUZZAH!

Phoebus, a captain in the King's Guard, mocks the hunchback.
Don't worry, ladies. I'll keep you safe from the creature.
The ugliest man in Paris!
Hurray, Quasimodo! Our Pope of Fools!
HUZZAH!
Poor creature! He can't even hear our cheers!

In the nearby plaza, Esmeralda dances for the crowd as part of the festivities.
So this is Esmeralda.
Who is that lovely woman?
She's a wicked gypsy. Like the ones that stole my baby!
Count to ten, Djali.
Esmeralda's pet goat, Djali, performs a trick for the crowd.

How did the goat do that? That's black magic!
Be quiet, Sister Gudule!
Everyone knows you're crazy!
Look! It's the Pope of Fools!
That poor man.
The beautiful girl is all alone in the world. Only I can help her.

CHAPTER 2
ATTACK!
Claude Frollo, Quasimodo's master, has seen enough.
!
On your knees!
The hunchback is almost completely deaf, but he understands his master's angry gestures.

As the festival ends, Gringoire the poet makes sure that Esmeralda reaches home. The streets of Paris can be dangerous.

The streets of Paris are indeed dangerous . . .
You're right, Djali, a man is following us.
Grab her!
Ahhhhhh!!!
Quasimodo dares not question his master.

Let her go!
Help me, please!
Frollo quickly leaves the scene.
Master? Where are you?

A few streets away . . .
BAAAAAAH! BAAAAAAH!
Look, Captain!
That's the gypsy girl's pet!
But where is she?
!
Djali leads the King's Guards to save Esmeralda.
Grab the hunchback, men!

Don't let him go!
He's strong as an ox.
Are you hurt, my dear? What is your name?
Esmeralda, sir.
Call me Phoebus.
What should we do with this beast, captain?
Throw him in jail.

Now then, Esmeralda.
What happened? Where is the girl?
She's gone, sir.
That beautiful girl. I hope she is safe!

High above, in the Cathedral of Notre Dame . . .
That beautiful girl. Only I can save her soul!

CHAPTER 3

CRUELTY AND KINDNESS

Now, put him on the rack!
Why are they hurting me?
Master! Help me, please!

The cold-hearted Frollo leaves Quasimodo to his suffering.

W-a-a-ter! Water!

Ha-ha-ha!

The hunchback wants some water!

Only Esmeralda takes pity on him.
Here, have some of this.
Gypsy witch!
She's a child snatcher, like the others!
Until this moment, Quasimodo has never known kindness.

CHAPTER 4

ESMERALDA ON TRIAL

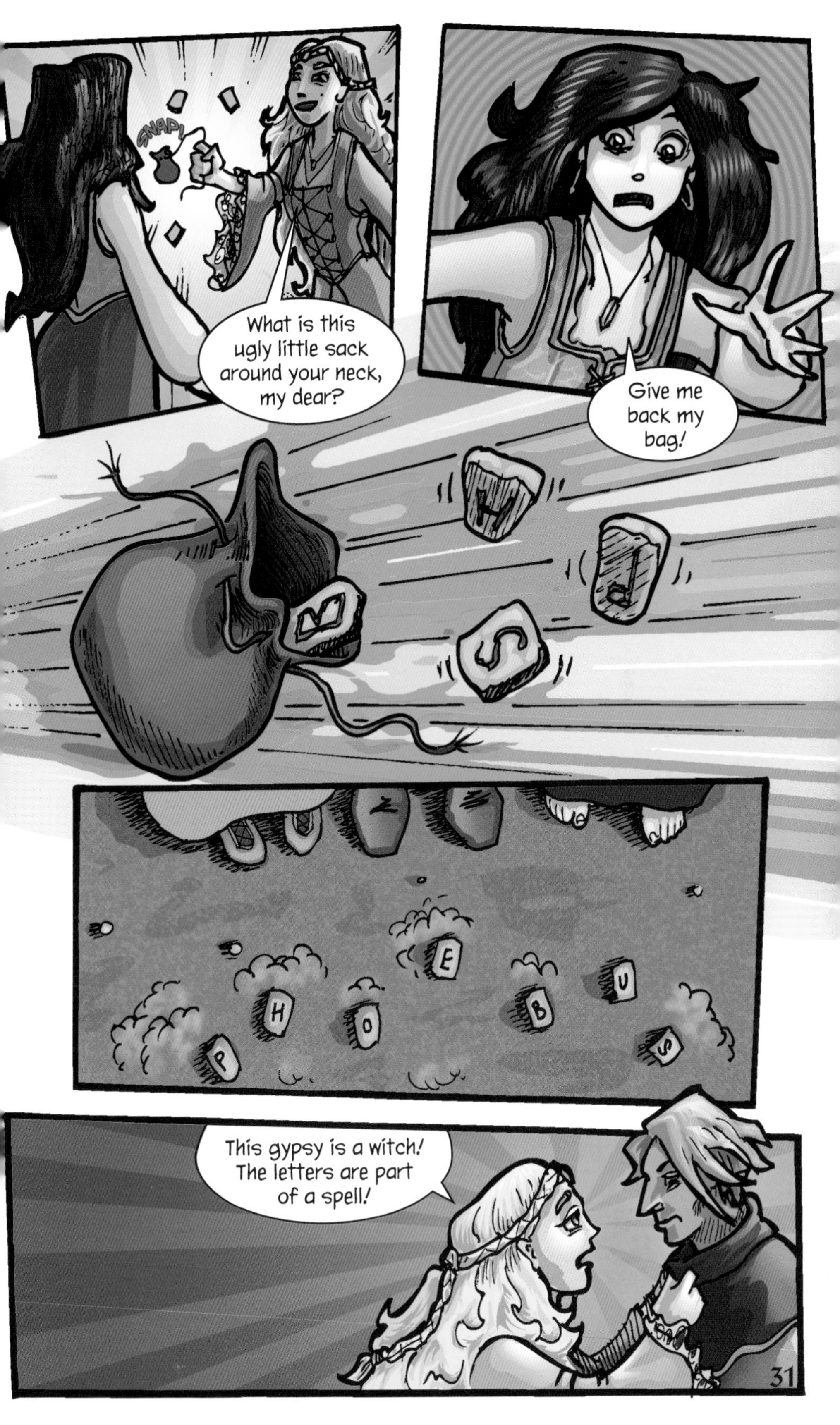
SNAP!
What is this ugly little sack around your neck, my dear?
Give me back my bag!
This gypsy is a witch! The letters are part of a spell!

A watchful eye gazes down from high in the cathedral.
There, there, Fleur-de-Lys. It was only a trick.
I'll stage a little "trick" of my own.

WHA!?!
Why is Quasimodo down there? I must reach the gypsy girl before he does!
What is going on?
She's gone!

Where is Esmeralda?
I don't know, Master Frollo.
Did she leave with the captain?
No. But she might be back at her inn.
Frollo travels the dark streets of Paris with an even darker plan in mind.
Later that night, near Esmeralda's inn . . .

THOK!
AAAAAAAHHHHH
No!
Somebody help! He's dead!
Seize her! We'll come back for the body later.

The next morning, Esmeralda is tried for murder and witchcraft.
She stabbed a man dead.
Right in the back, in cold blood.
Why did you kill this man?
You were caught twisting a knife in a man's back.
I was pulling it out. I was trying to save him.

I've heard enough. Take her to the torture room!

After a dreadful hour, Esmeralda appears before the judge again.
Now, do you confess to murder? Do you admit to being a witch?
Yes, I confess! Just don't torture me anymore!
Death by hanging!

She is too kind to die. I will protect her.

CHAPTER 5
RESCUE
In jail, time passes slowly for Esmeralda.
How did this all happen? Am I dreaming?
Perhaps I will see my Phoebus again in death.
Esmeralda!

You! You're the evil man that killed Phoebus.
Hush, child. I did it for us.
What do you mean?

Poor girl. You don't understand true love when you see it.
I will never love you! You must be mad!

And you are a fool. Your Phoebus is dead!

Phoebus was not dead. He lived through the stabbing, and had been in the countryside, recovering.
I've missed Paris. It's good to be back. I think it's high time we planned our wedding.
What is happening today?
That gypsy killed a man. She is about to be hanged.
Esmeralda? Who would she kill?
They don't know. They say the body was gone when the guards went to pick it up.

The guards lead Esmeralda past Notre Dame.
Kill her! Hang the witch!
Hang the witch!

Can it be?
Phoebus! Is that you?
BANG

He's alive! I must go to him!
Please, that's the man they say I killed. But he's alive! My Phoebus is alive!

As Esmeralda prepares to accept her fate, Quasimodo prepares to protect her.
Look out!
Oh no!

Quasimodo races back to the cathedral.
Sanctuary! Sanctuary!
Run!
Faster!

CHAPTER 6
IN THE CATHEDRAL

Later that day, Quasimodo brings Esmeralda some food and clothing that was left on the steps of Notre Dame.
Why did you save me?
You were kind to me when no one else was.

It's all right, Quasimodo. You can stay.

RING
RING
RING
Such glorious music. Paris is lucky to hear it every day.
Every morning and every night, Esmeralda listens to the song of Quasimodo's bells!

RING
Esmeralda spends her time singing. She sings about finding her parents some day. Quasimodo can't hear the songs, but he loves watching her.
I will do **anything** to protect her.
One day, Quasimodo gives Esmeralda a special whistle he made.

In case you ever need help.

Thank you, dear friend.

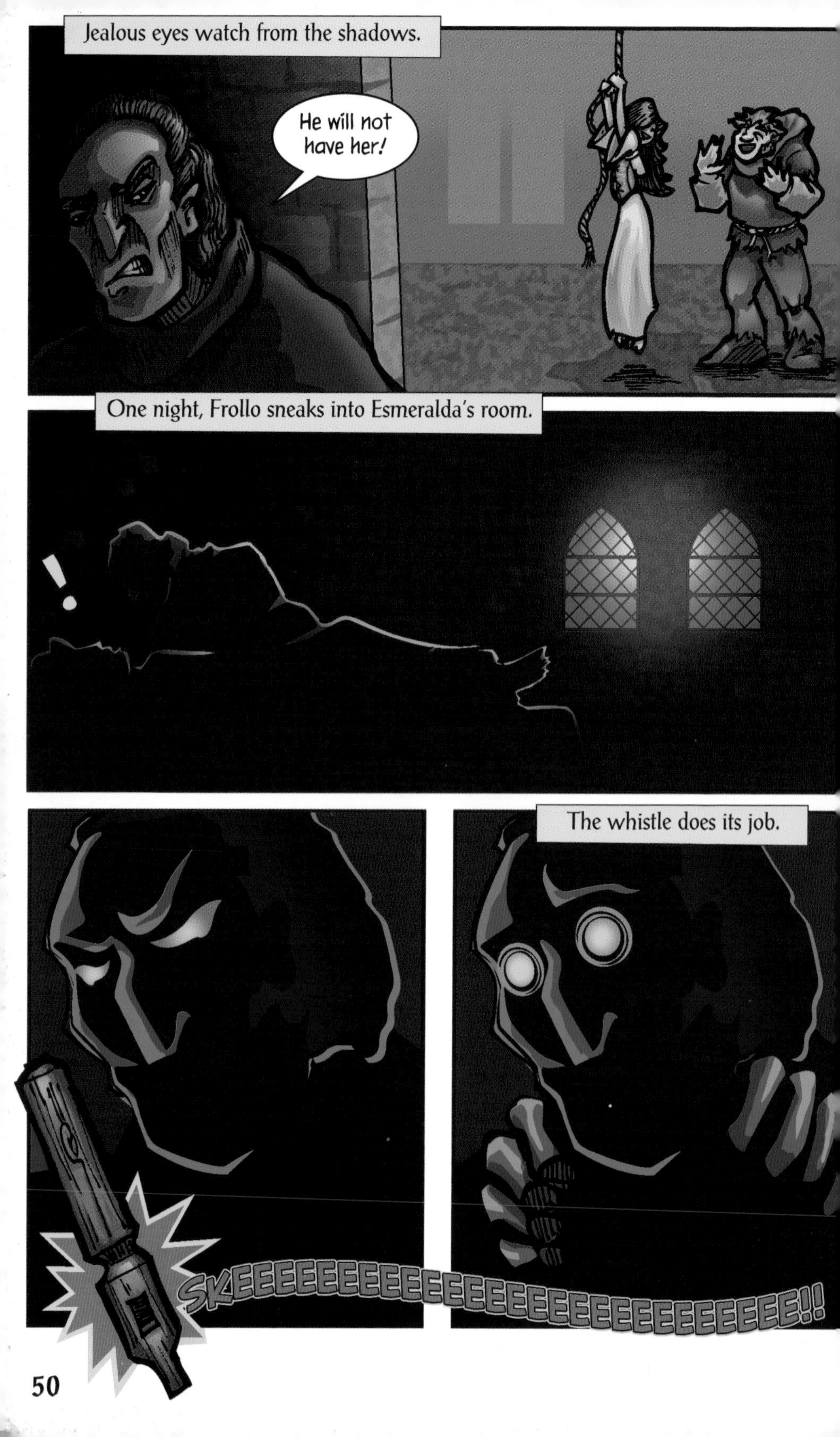
Jealous eyes watch from the shadows.
He will not have her!
One night, Frollo sneaks into Esmeralda's room.
!
The whistle does its job.
SKEEEEEEEEEEEEEEEEEEEEEEEEEEEEE!!

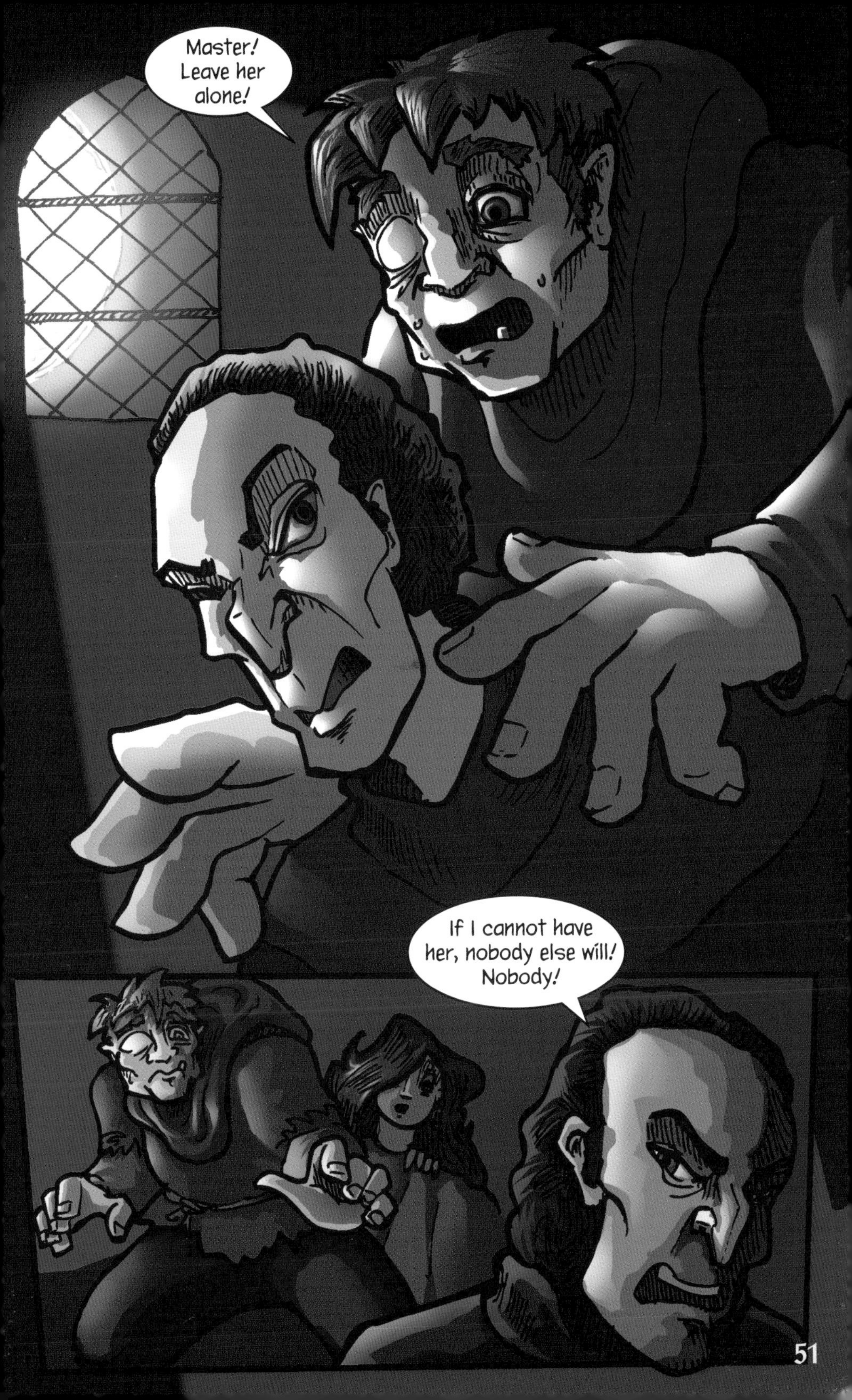
Master! Leave her alone!
If I cannot have her, nobody else will! Nobody!

Frollo sets his plan in motion. He talks to Esmeralda's friends.
We must save her.
The King's Guards plan to seize Esmeralda from the cathedral. She is no longer safe.
We'll all help.
Protect the innocent!
Save Esmeralda!

Quasimodo cannot understand the crowd's words. He thinks they plan to kill Esmeralda.
Look out! It's molten lead!
When the King's Guards arrive, Quasimodo thinks they've come to help.
Inside Esmeralda's room . . .
Find the gypsy witch!
Esmeralda?

CHAPTER 7
THE BITTER END
Frollo captured Esmeralda during the attack on Notre Dame.
You have two choices. Say you love me, or be hanged!
I'd rather die than love you!
Take her to the hangman, Sister Gudule.
With pleasure, Frollo. This girl deserves to die.

Gypsies stole my baby girl! You're one of them, and you're all evil!
I'm sorry about your baby, but I haven't hurt anyone!
The gypsies stole me as a child, too. Please, you must let me go!

This is all I have left of my child. I pulled it off her as your people ripped her from my arms.
Look! This shoe was mine when I was a baby! One of the gypsies saved it for me. She said the other one was lost forever. The shoes are a perfect match!

Mother!
My child! At last!
Oh, how I have longed for this day!
Don't take my child away again! I just found her!
The King's Guards take Esmeralda prisoner.
Be careful, Mother!
Your time is up, you crazy old hag!
KRAK
No!

Quasimodo searches for Esmeralda.
He runs up to the north tower for a
clear view of the whole city.

Look at that, Quasimodo. There is your beautiful gypsy!
ESMERALDA!

You killed her!
AAAAAAHHHH

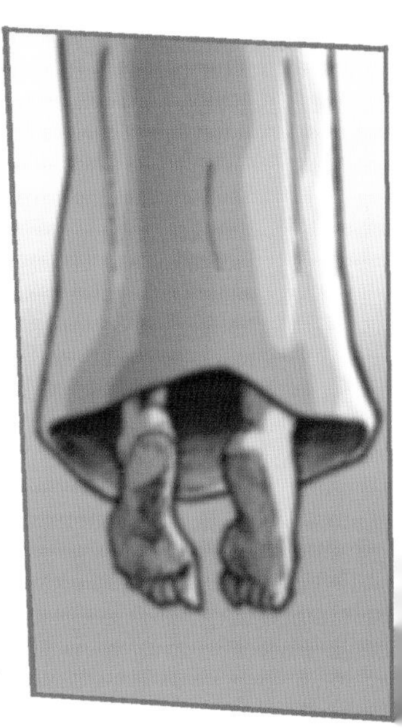

After that terrible day, no one ever saw the hunchback of Notre Dame again.

Two years later, a grave digger opens the crypt near Notre Dame. He finds the strangest thing.

Two skeletons lie in the darkness. One belongs to a young woman, and the other to a strange misshapen creature. They sleep near each other, in peace, forever.

ABOUT VICTOR HUGO

Victor Hugo was born 26 February, 1802, in Besançon, France. As a child, Hugo's family moved often because his father was in the military. Later, in his adult years, Hugo married and had four children. He worked as a writer and produced many plays, poems, and novels. He is considered one of the greatest French writers of all time. When Hugo died on 22 May, 1885, two million people attended his funeral in Paris.

Hugo was inspired to write *The Hunchback of Notre Dame* because Paris's famous cathedral was in bad shape. He wanted to draw attention to Notre Dame, and hoped that people would remember its beauty and work to repair it.

ABOUT THE AUTHOR

L. L. Owens has written more than 45 books of fiction and non-fiction for young readers, including *American Justice: Seven Famous Trials of the 20th Century.* She enjoys reading great books, cooking, and listening to music. Ms Owens lives in Seattle, USA and loves to explore the Pacific Northwest of the United States.

ABOUT THE ILLUSTRATOR

Greg Rebis was born in New York, USA but mostly grew up in central Florida. After working in civic government, pizza delivery, music retail, and proofreading, he eventually began to work in publishing, film, and graphics. He currently lives and studies in Rhode Island, USA and still loves art, sci-fi, and video games.

GLOSSARY

amulet (AM-u-let) - a stone, gem, or charm worn to keep away evil spirits

cathedral (kuh-THEE-druhl) - a large, important church

crypt (KRIPT) - underground area where people were buried; many crypts were attached to a church

deaf (DEF) - unable to hear well or unable to hear at all

deformed (di-FORMD) - shaped oddly or differently from normal

gambler (GAM-bler) - a person who bets money all of the time

gypsy (JIP-see) - a person who wanders from place to place, often without a home

innocent (IN-nuh-sent) - not guilty or not at fault

sanctuary (SANGK-choo-er-ee) - a place of safety or protection

trinkets (TRINK-ets) - small, pretty things

vibrations (vye-BRAY-shuns) - shaking or trembling movements

GOOD AND EVIL IN THE FIFTEENTH CENTURY

The Hunchback of Notre Dame takes place in Paris, France, at the end of the 1400s. The author, Victor Hugo, set the book at this time to show how differently, and often unfairly, people were treated at that time.

A long time ago, people believed that things in the world were either good or evil. If good things happened, people went to church to thank God. But when bad things happened, people blamed witchcraft and black magic. Many people believed that witches and wizards had the power to place evil spells on people.

If people committed a crime, they were tortured, or hurt, for punishment. One punishment was stretching people on a rack. The rack pulled people's arms and legs, putting them in great pain. If a crime was severe, people might be executed, or killed. Hanging people was a common form of execution.

Unfortunately, in the 1400s, many people were punished unfairly. Some people were accused of things they did not do. If someone acted differently than everyone else, that person could be killed for being a witch. Victor Hugo wanted his readers to see that things have changed since those earlier times, and sometimes things change for the better.

DISCUSSION QUESTIONS

1. At the end of the story, a grave digger finds the skeletons of Quasimodo and Esmeralda in the same place. Why was Quasimodo's skeleton there? How did it get there?

2. Why does Quasimodo rescue Esmeralda?

3. Why does Frollo have Esmeralda arrested for something she didn't do?

4. How does Esmeralda find her mother?

5. People often say, "You shouldn't judge a book by its cover." What does this saying mean? How does it relate to Quasimodo?

WRITING PROMPTS

1. *The Hunchback of Notre Dame* is a story about kindness and loyalty. Write about someone who showed kindness or loyalty when you were in trouble. How did this person's kindness make you feel?

2. Describe your favourite character in the story. What does this person look like? Is this person kind or evil? How does this person act?

3. Imagine that you lived in a giant cathedral, apart from other people. Describe what your day would be like. How would you eat? Where would you sleep? Would you have special hiding places inside the cathedral? Write and tell about it. Describe your cathedral.

OTHER BOOKS

Gulliver's Travels

Lemuel Gulliver always dreamed of sailing across seas, but he never could have imagined the places his travels would take him. On the island of Lilliput, he is captured by tiny creatures no more than six inches tall. In a country of Blefuscu, he is nearly squashed by an army of giants. His adventures could be the greatest tales ever told, if he survives long enough to tell them.

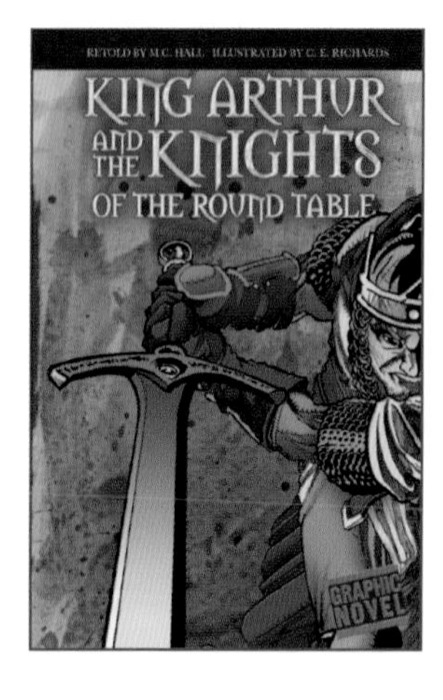

King Arthur and the Knights of the Round Table

In a world of wizards, giants, and dragons, King Arthur and the Knights of the Round Table are the kingdom of Camelot's only defence against the threatening forces of evil. Fighting battles and saving those in need, the Knights of the Round Table can defeat every enemy but one – themselves!

Treasure Island

Jim Hawkins had no idea what he was getting into when the pirate Billy Bones showed up at the doorstep of his mother's inn. When Billy dies suddenly, Jim is left to unlock his old sea chest, which reveals money, a journal, and a treasure map. Joined by a band of honourable men, Jim sets sail on a dangerous voyage to locate the loot on a faraway island. The violent sea is only one of the dangers they face. They soon encounter a band of bloodthirsty pirates determined to make the treasure their own!

Robin Hood

Robin Hood and his Merrie Men are the heroes of Sherwood Forest. Taking from the rich and giving to the poor, Robin Hood and his loyal followers fight for the downtrodden and oppressed. As they outwit the cruel Sheriff of Nottingham, Robin Hood and his Merrie Men are led on a series of exciting adventures.

GRAPHIC REVOLVE

If you have enjoyed this story, there are many more exciting tales for you to discover in the Graphic Revolve collection...

20,000 Leagues Under the Sea

Black Beauty

Dracula

Frankenstein

Gulliver's Travels

The Hound of the Baskervilles

The Hunchback of Notre Dame

King Arthur and the Knights of the Round Table

Robin Hood

The Strange Case of Dr Jekyll and Mr Hyde

Treasure Island

The War of the Worlds